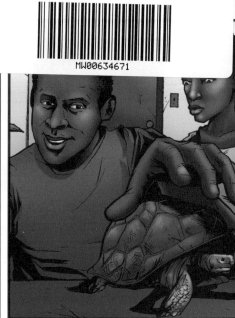

Attainment's

Social Story Readers

Illustrated by Nick Runge | Colors by Gabe Eltaeb

Shelia Lechler
Debbie Semple

By Debbie Semple and Shelia Lechler

Edited by Tom Kinney

Graphic Design by Lynn Chrisman

An Attainment Company Publication

© 2006 Attainment Company, Inc., All rights reserved.

Printed in China

ISBN: 1-57861-574-7

Attainment Company, Inc.

P.O. Box 930160

Verona, Wisconsin 53593-0160 USA

1-800-327-4269

www.AttainmentCompany.com

Table of Contents

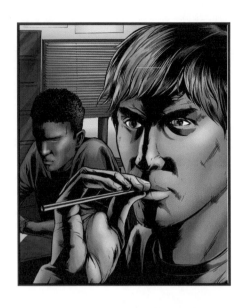

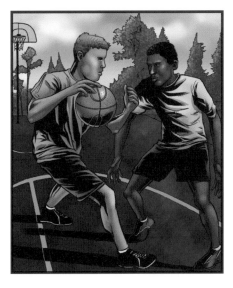

Try Your Best

It was the first day of school.

Try Your Best

It was the first day of school. Steven and Kaci were in Mrs. Allison's class last year. They were happy to be back. They knew all the rules and were glad to see their friends again.

Gina was a new student in Mrs. Allison's class. She didn't know anyone, and she was scared. She was trying to get Steven and Kaci to notice her. She wanted them to be her friends.

She felt like a fish in a bowl. What if she made a mistake? She was afraid to answer any questions. What if she didn't know the right answers?

Try Your Best

Mrs. Allison asked everyone in the class to come to group time. Gina was nervous, but she tried not to show it. All the students sat in chairs around a big table. Gina wondered what would happen next.

Mrs. Allison said, "The first thing we are going to do today is called a pep rally. Since Steven was in this class last year, he is going to help me."

Steven knew just what to do. He got up and went to stand in front of six giant posters. Mrs. Allison gave Steven a long pointed stick.

She said, "Steven will lead our pep rally today. First, he will read each poster, and then, we will all read it out loud together."

Steven read the first poster. He said, "I like myself, and I'm great!"

Mrs. Allison said, "Now, everyone say the same thing all together."

All the students repeated the sentence. "I like myself, and I'm great," they mumbled.

"Oh, no!" said Mrs. Allison, "I need you to say it very loud! Yell it out, and bang your hands on the table like drums in a real pep rally."

Gina was surprised! Her new teacher wanted her to yell in class! Could this get any better?

All the students yelled and banged their hands on the table, "I like myself, and I'm great!"

It was so loud! Gina thought the roof was going to pop off.

The students listened to Steven. He read each poster, and everyone yelled them back at him.

Try Your Best

"I'm super good and getting better!"

"I always try my best!"

"I'm always nice!"

"I'm the greatest person in the world!"

"I'm so proud of myself!"

After the pep rally, Gina felt good. She thought to herself, "I do like myself, and I like this class, too."

CHAPTER 3 When the pep rally was over, Mrs. Allison asked if anyone wanted to take a risk? All the new students were confused, but Kaci raised her hand and said, "I will!"

Kaci went up to the board in front of the room. Mrs. Allison put a math problem on the board and

asked Kaci to find the answer. Kaci tried her best, but she made a mistake and wrote the wrong answer.

Mrs. Allison showed Kaci the right way to do the problem, and Kaci went back to sit down at the table.

Mrs. Allison said, "Sometimes, it is not good to take a risk! There are good risks and bad risks. In this class, it's a good thing to take a risk! We have to try so that we can learn. I want everyone to know that I am proud of Kaci! She made a mistake. And that's okay, because she tried her best!"

CHAPTER 4

Later that day during free time, Steven was writing on the board. He wrote, "I like myself, and I'm greta!"

He didn't spell all the words right, but that's okay. Do you know which word was wrong?

Change is My Friend

Brice thought summer was the best season of the year.

Change is My Friend

Brice thought summer was the best season of the year. He didn't have to get up early or rush around to get ready for school. He could sleep late, watch TV, swim, and fish. He even caught a turtle at the lake. He decided to keep it as a pet. He put the turtle in an aquarium in his room.

Brice called the turtle Ninja, but his younger sister and brother had their own ideas about a good name for the new family pet. His sister thought the turtle was a girl and wanted to name her Myrtle. His brother said that the turtle was fast and a great jumper. He wanted him to be named Hurdle. Sometimes, Brice worried about his brother. Everyone knows turtles are not fast!

Social Story Readers

Change is My Friend

In spite of his sister and brother, Brice enjoyed himself. However, summer was over too quickly. He was sad to see his summer fun coming to an end, but looked forward to school starting again in the fall. The best part of school was when his class went on community trips. His favorite was bowling!

Just before school started again, Brice's dad got a new job! His whole family moved to a different town. Brice had to leave all his friends and go to a new school. What if his new class didn't go bowling?

Change is My Friend

CHAPTER 3 On his first day in the new school, Brice was worried until he met his new teacher. Her name was Mrs. Allison. She was really nice and helped him to feel better about being in a different classroom.

Brice also found out that he was not the only new student. The other new students were Gina, Hannah, and Jason.

Social Story Readers

Change is My Friend

Mrs. Allison asked the new students to introduce themselves to the class.

Jason became so scared when Mrs. Allison talked to him that he went and stood in the corner facing the wall. He was hiding from everyone! He was shy and embarrassed to be around new people.

Hannah was excited to talk to everyone. She rattled on and on until they all became tired of listening. She went up really close to each person and talked right next to their face. They had to back up to get away from her.

Change is My Friend

Gina was calm and cool. She talked quietly, shook each person's hand and said, "Hi! My name is Gina. I hope we can all be friends."

CHAPTER 5

After Brice saw each person introduce themselves, he knew just what to do. He decided to do the same things as Gina. He smiled and was friendly to everyone. He shook hands, looked them in the eye, and said, "Hi! I'm Brice. It is so nice to meet you."

Oh, and by the way, Brice found out that his new class went bowling every Tuesday.

It's About More Than Chores

Corey's parents wanted him to learn about responsibility.

It's About More Than Chores

Corey's parents wanted him to learn about responsibility. He wasn't even sure he knew what the word meant, but it didn't sound good. His Mom and Dad explained to him that responsibility was a very important thing.

They said they would like to be able to trust him and depend on him to do things for them. He could help around the house and stay there on his own with a set of rules to follow. They would know that he was growing up and learning to be independent. He could have his own apartment some day!

Social Story Readers

It's About More Than Chores

Corey had been listening to his teacher, Mrs. Allison, talk about responsibility at school, and he thought he could handle it. After all, his parents were

supposed to be responsible weren't they, and they never did anything that they didn't want to do.

They didn't have to ask permission to go anywhere, and they had their own money, a house, and their own wheels! Being an adult couldn't be that hard, could it?

It's About More Than Chores

Corey's Dad said he thought that Corey was becoming mature, and he could handle some responsibilities after school. He made a list of chores for Corey to finish before he was allowed to go outside. Chores!!? Corey really hated chores and wondered why he had to do all the work!

Who knew you had to work to be responsible? He didn't like this, but he promised to do his chores first before anything else.

Social Story Readers

It's About More Than Chores

Corey got off the bus after school. He had his own house key, and he didn't lose it today. He was proud of himself! Yesterday, Mrs. Allison had to go to the gym to find his key before he could get on the bus. He lost it during P.E. Today, he made sure it was safely on a string around his neck!

When he opened the door and went in the house, he put down his backpack. He went straight to the list of chores. He knew this would be easy! No problem!

He read these things on the list:

1. Take out the trash.
2. Make your bed.
3. Feed and water the dog.

Not so hard to do, right?

CHAPTER 4

As Corey went into the kitchen to take out the trash, he saw a big donut on the cabinet. He imagined that donut was talking to him. The donut was calling his name. It said, "Corey, come have a snack! I know you are hungry because you worked hard at school all day!"

Well, Corey knew that was true, and he sat down and ate the donut. He forgot that he didn't take out the trash!

It's About More Than Chores

He went into the bedroom to do the next thing on his list of chores. When he was there, he decided it couldn't hurt to watch TV while he made the bed. His favorite cartoon show was on, "Rob and Bob eat Corn on the Cob!"

He watched that show, and it was so funny that he forgot to make his bed.

He was just watching the next TV show when his parents came home. His parents looked kind of mad! Do you know why?

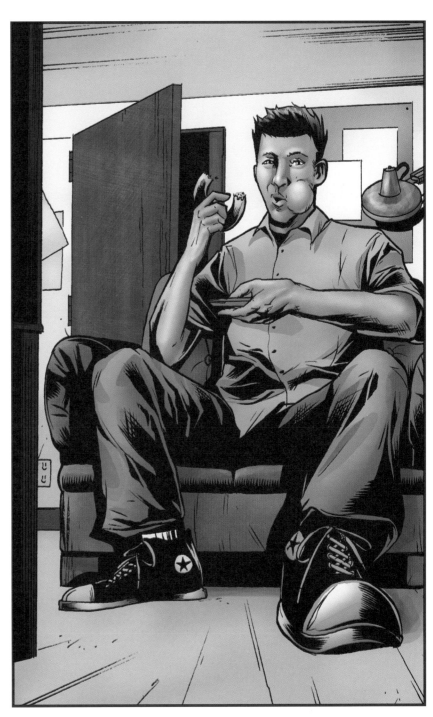

CHAPTER 5

Corey's dog, Sir Barksalot, was so hungry and thirsty!

You're Being Watched

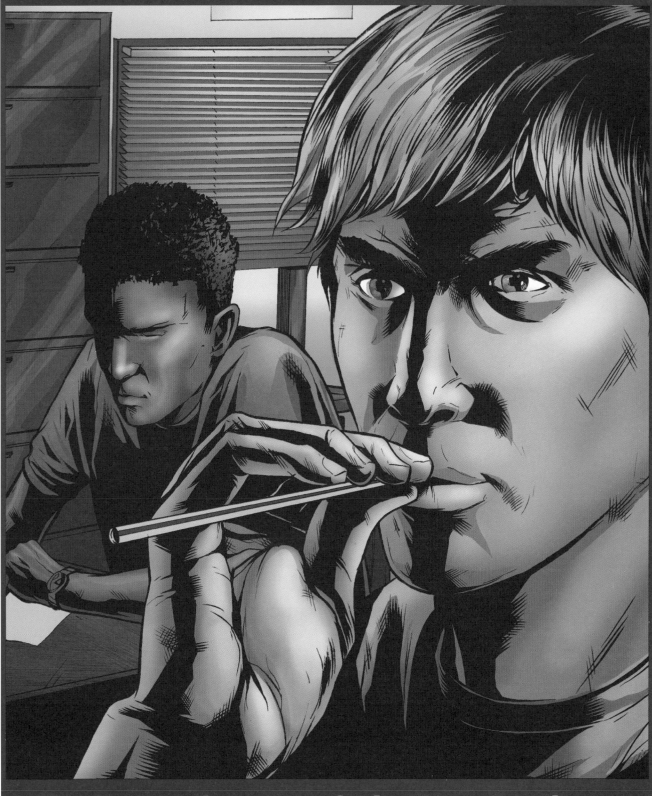

Rob took careful aim and......

You're Being Watched

CHAPTER 1 Rob took careful aim and blew a spit wad at his friend, Jeff. He missed Jeff by a few inches and hit his teacher, Mrs. Allison in the back of the head. Mrs. Allison slowly turned to look at all the students. Rob tried his best to look innocent. He thought if he was very still, he might become invisible. Maybe Mrs. Allison would not know he was the guilty one.

Social Story Readers

You're Being Watched

The other students in Mrs. Allison's class were waiting to see what happened next. Even Rob's friends hoped he would get into trouble for hitting Mrs. Allison. Rob's friend, Melissa, was tired of Rob's sneaky tricks. Jeff wanted to be Rob's friend, but it was hard to like someone who sent spit whizzing by your ear. Rob caused problems for the whole class. It was the last straw for Rob in more ways than one.

You're Being Watched

Most of the students had seen the whole thing, and they only wished Mrs. Allison could have seen it. They were tempted to tattle, but knew it was against the rules. They had one hope. There was a rumor going around that Mrs. Allison had eyes in the back of her head because she always knew who did everything. Most likely, those eyes were right where the spit wad landed.

CHAPTER 4

Mrs. Allison didn't really have an extra set of eyes in the back of her head, but she was very smart, and she knew right away who had thrown the spit wad. This was not the first time Rob had caused problems in her class.

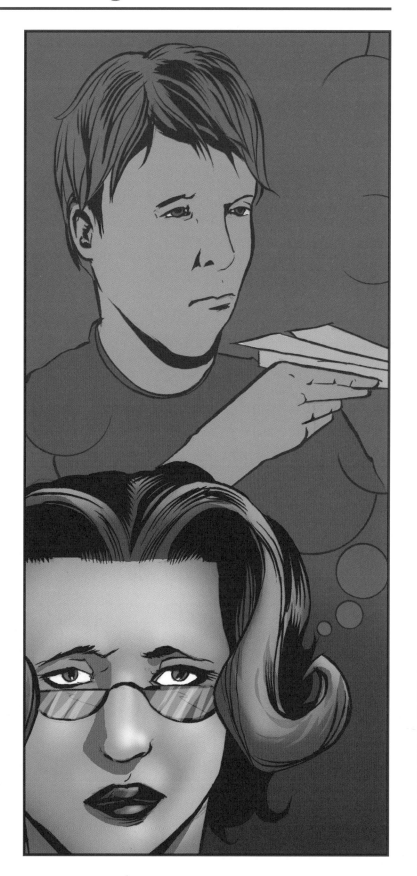

You're Being Watched

Mrs. Allison talked to Rob about the bad things he had been doing in class. She told him he was not allowed to keep the other students from learning. She talked to him about making the right choices. Rob really listened to her, and decided to change the way he acted in school. He wanted to be a better person. He followed all the rules for the rest of the day at school and Mrs. Allison was very happy.

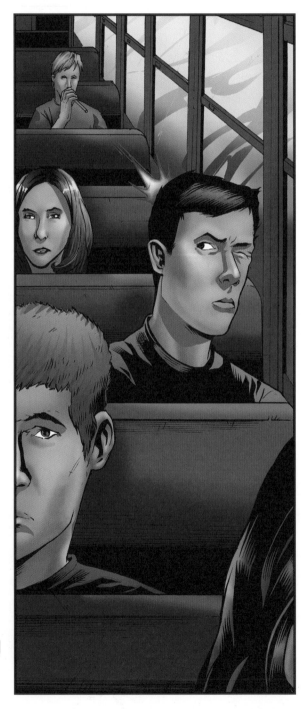

After school on the bus, Rob was sitting in the back seat. Jeff was sitting in a seat at the front of the bus. You will never guess what happened next. Rob blew another spit wad at Jeff. He thought it would be okay because Mrs. Allison couldn't see him, and he wouldn't get in trouble. Was Rob really trying to be a better person?

Choose Your Attitude

Have you ever had
one of those days?

Choose Your Attitude

Hannah was having one of those days when nothing seemed to go her way. It started early in the morning!

"Hannah, wake up! Rise and Shine! The bus will be here soon!" her mom called. Hannah was very tired, and she dug deeper under the covers just to get a little more sleep.

Her mom came back a second time and found her still sleeping. She shook her awake and said, "Hannah! I thought you were up and getting ready for school! The bus will be here in a few minutes! You have to hurry!"

Choose Your Attitude

Hannah jumped out of bed like a track star running a race. She ran two laps around the house before she was awake enough to realize she wasn't in her PE class.

Choose Your Attitude

She pulled on her clothes and jammed her feet into her tennis shoes. She grabbed her lunch and ran out the door toward the bus. She didn't have time to tie her shoes and tripped on her shoelaces.

When she fell, her lunch went flying into the air! Her dog, Frisbee, jumped up and grabbed her sandwich before it ever hit the ground. He quickly ran around the house and buried it in the backyard!

When Hannah got off the bus, she realized that she had forgotten her homework. She wondered if Frisbee buried it, too.

Choose Your Attitude

When Hannah reached her classroom, the teacher, Mrs. Allison, reminded everyone that today was school picture day. Who knew things could get worse? In her rush to get ready, Hannah's clothes didn't match, her hair was uncombed, and her eye was swollen shut from her fall in the yard.

Choose Your Attitude

CHAPTER 4

By some small miracle, Hannah made it through the picture taking ordeal, and the camera didn't break.

The final blow came when Hannah was in line in the cafeteria, and the kid in front of her took the last corny dog. Life just isn't fair!!!

Hey Bob, Do Your Job!

Everyone in Mrs. Allison's class had jobs to do in the cafeteria.

Hey Bob, Do Your Job!

CHAPTER 1 Everyday the students in Mrs. Allison's class had jobs to do in the cafeteria. They worked as teams with two people helping each other do one job. Jen and Bob were a team, and they were in charge of cleaning four sets of tables and chairs.

CHAPTER 2 Bob hated doing work and always tried to think of ways to get out of every job. He used a lot of tricks to make people think he couldn't do the work. He worked very slowly and walked like an old man. He barely moved his arms and legs and looked like he was in slow motion. The only times Bob ever moved quickly was when

he ran to the bathroom or pushed and shoved his way to the front of the lunch line.

CHAPTER 3

Bob loved to pretend to do the wrong things on a job. He acted as if he couldn't find the cleaning rags. It seemed like he didn't know how to make soapy water. He forgot to wring out his rag and left a soapy trail of water on the cafeteria floor.

If anyone walked through the cafeteria, Bob would stop and talk to them for a long time. Sometimes he would do a little dance and sling his rag around and around in a circle. While Bob was up to his tricks, Jen was working hard and fast. She tried her best and did a great job! She cleaned three sets of tables and chairs while Bob only cleaned one set. She did a lot more work than Bob. Somehow, that didn't seem right!!

CHAPTER 4

Would you rather be on a team with Bob or Jen?

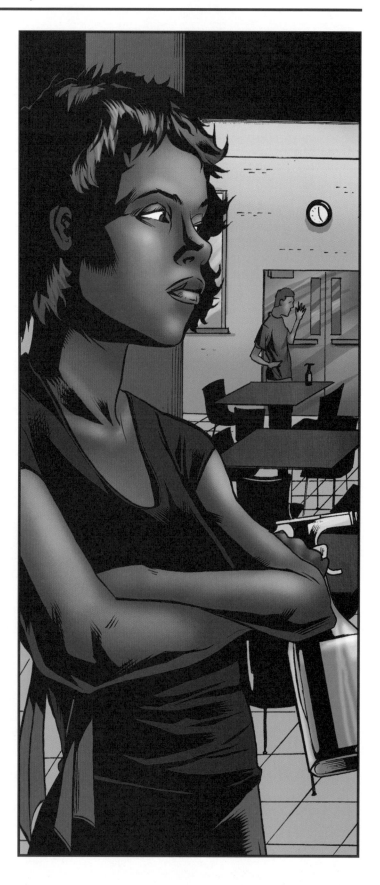

The Wrath of Jen

Jen and Bob were teammates.

The Wrath of Jen

CHAPTER 1 Jen and Bob were teammates on a cleaning job at school. They were in charge of four sets of tables and chairs. Jen was doing the best job possible, but Bob was not doing his share of the work. Jen became very angry as she finished the job. It just wasn't right for Bob to take advantage of her!

CHAPTER 2 Jen thought about telling Mrs. Allison about what Bob was doing, but she knew it was against the rules to tattle on her friends every minute. She didn't know how to

The Wrath of Jen

solve the problem of Bob's lazy work habits. He was using her to do all his work! Her anger was building and building. She became very upset. She didn't know how to handle her feelings.

CHAPTER 3

She started to think of ways to get back at Bob. She imagined pouring the cleaning water over his head. She wanted to call him a lazy bum and tell him to do his half of the work. Maybe you can help her decide what to do!

CHAPTER 4

If you worked with Bob, would you:

1. Do something to get even with him?

2. Only clean two tables and leave the other two tables dirty?

3. Do the best you can and clean all the tables so the job is finished?

Dale's Cover Up

Dale was having a hard time with his work at school.

Dale's Cover Up

CHAPTER 1 Dale was having a hard time with his work at school. He was really trying, but he just couldn't do it.

The other students were getting ahead of him. He felt like the last runner in a never-ending race.

CHAPTER 2 To hide his embarrassment, he would do things in class to get bad attention. He never turned in his homework. When he took a test, he wrote silly answers in all the blanks like the Easter Bunny, the Tooth Fairy, Bigfoot, and Jar Jar Binks.

He tried to cause trouble for the other kids, too. Mysterious things happened. The girl who sat next to him stood

Dale's Cover Up

up and fell on her face because her shoelaces were tied together. A boy's pen suddenly fell apart and spilled ink all over his desk and clothes.

Even the teacher, Mrs. French, was not safe from his tricks. Mrs. French was getting on in years, and her eyesight was poor. Dale replaced her dry erase marker with a permanent marker.

Facts about "dangerous weather" became forever stuck on her dry erase board.

Mrs. French had an itch, and when she scratched it, she accidentally put a permanent dot on her nose that wouldn't wash off for six weeks.

Dale's Cover Up

CHAPTER 3 In spite of her poor eyesight and the dot on her nose, Mrs. French was pretty shrewd about her students. She realized that there was another problem going on with Dale, and she wanted to help him.

She had a meeting with his parents, and together, they decided he needed to be in a different classroom where he could get extra help with his school work.

Don't Put Underwear on Your Head

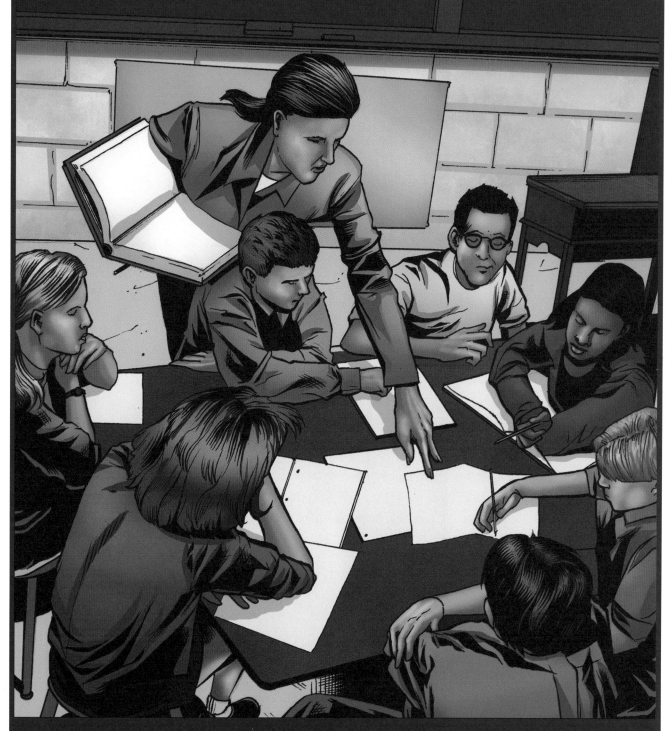

Dale went to a new classroom.

Don't Put Underwear on Your Head

CHAPTER 1 Dale went to a new classroom. He liked his new teacher, and he quickly made new friends.

He was so relieved that his school work was not too hard. He was doing a better job on his reading and math. He went on the bus out into the community. He learned about job skills and good behavior. Dale didn't think he had to do bad things to get attention anymore. He was proud of himself.

Social Story Readers

Don't Put Underwear on Your Head

CHAPTER 2 Dale had just one problem. Sometimes, he would see his old friends around school. Most of them would wave and say, "Hi," but not Victor. Victor thought it was funny seeing Dale in a different class. He laughed and told everyone Dale was in the "dumb" class.

CHAPTER 3 Dale wanted to fight back. Just when he was about to give Victor a knuckle sandwich, his friend Mike came up to them. "Get lost, Victor!" he said, "You are just jealous because you don't get to go on the bus and do fun things like Dale's class. You are the dumb one for being so mean!"

Don't Put Underwear on Your Head

CHAPTER 4 Mike put his arm around Dale and said, "Come on, friend! Let's just ignore him! Kids who say mean things to other people just don't like themselves enough. My mom says to imagine them with their underwear on their heads, laugh and walk away!"

Don't Worry About It

Lori worried about little things too much.

Don't Worry About It

CHAPTER 1

Lori was fourteen years old. She was a good student and a nice person, but she worried too much. She worried about little things all the time.

Social Story Readers

Don't Worry About It

CHAPTER 2 She had certain things she carried in her purse, and if she didn't have them close to her, she became upset. She thought everyone wanted to steal her purse. It became such a problem that her teacher asked her to leave her purse at home.

Don't Worry About It

CHAPTER 3

She started wearing clothes with big pockets and crammed all of her things in her pockets. She looked like an overstuffed teddy bear.

Don't Worry About It

Using the vending machines in the cafeteria was a joy to Lori, but deciding what to buy was a nightmare.

One day she made her decision, and the item she wanted to buy was sold out. She threw a temper tantrum. If the item became stuck in the machine, she cried big crocodile tears. The day she accidentally lost her money, everyone hoped it would never happen again!!

Don't Worry About It

Do you think that Lori worried about important things?

The Real Deal

Alyssa liked to sing.

The Real Deal

Alyssa liked to sing, but she didn't have a talent for singing. When she sang, she sounded like a cat when someone stepped on its tail. Even though Alyssa was not a good singer, it was her dream to grow up to become a famous rock star.

The Real Deal

CHAPTER 2

Alyssa talked about this goal for her life every minute of the day. She would run up to people and tell them about her great plans for her future.

She dyed her hair purple and wore black lipstick and nail polish. She wouldn't answer if you called her by her real name. She said that from now on she would be known as "Madonna".

The Real Deal

CHAPTER 3 All of her friends, teachers, and the coaches at school tried to avoid her, because they became tired of her endless obsession. If they saw her coming their way, they would turn and run. Even her closest friends didn't want to be with her anymore.

She forgot about her schoolwork and her responsibilities at home. She was too busy being a "star!"

The Real Deal

Her teachers and parents became worried about her. They knew that she was not concentrating on the things that she could really do well, because she was always obsessing about something that was impossible for her.

The Real Deal

CHAPTER 5

Was the goal that Alyssa had for her future something that could really happen?

All Tied Up and Nowhere to Go

Rodney was so excited.

All Tied Up and Nowhere to Go

Rodney was so excited! He was offered a job at a local factory. His job was to pack bottles into boxes so that trucks could take them to stores.

His boss, Mr. Travis, told him exactly how to do his work. Rodney was asked to stand by the conveyor belt as the bottles came by and put them in a box.

Mr. Travis wanted Rodney to put twelve bottles in each box, and fold down the four flaps on each side of the box. Mr. Travis told Rodney to seal each box with one long piece of packing tape. He wanted Rodney to stack up all the sealed boxes so that another worker would get them and put them on the truck.

Social Story Readers

All Tied Up and Nowhere to Go

Rodney was proud of the job he was doing, and he wanted to make sure he did everything the very best way.

He thought, "If I put thirteen bottles in each box, it will surely be much better than twelve!" Rodney left the conveyor belt and went to ask his boss if it would be O.K.

Mr. Travis said, "No, Rodney. I need you to put only twelve bottles in each box."

CHAPTER 3 Rodney ran back to the conveyor belt and saw a lot of bottles stacking up in a row. He should have quickly packed the bottles, but he just had one more question!

Rodney ran back to Mr. Travis and said, "Should all the bottles be turned exactly the same way in the box?"

Mr. Travis said, "No, Rodney! It doesn't matter which way you turn the bottles! Just put them in the box!"

Rodney said, "I just wanted to make sure," and he ran back quickly to the conveyor belt.

CHAPTER 4

By this time, many, many bottles were piling up to be packed into boxes, and Rodney was getting behind in his work. He hurried to pack the twelve bottles into a box. He folded the four flaps to close the box, and it was time to seal the box with tape.

Rodney had just one more question. He ran back to Mr. Travis and said, "Mr. Travis, don't you think it would be better if we used two pieces of tape instead of one?"

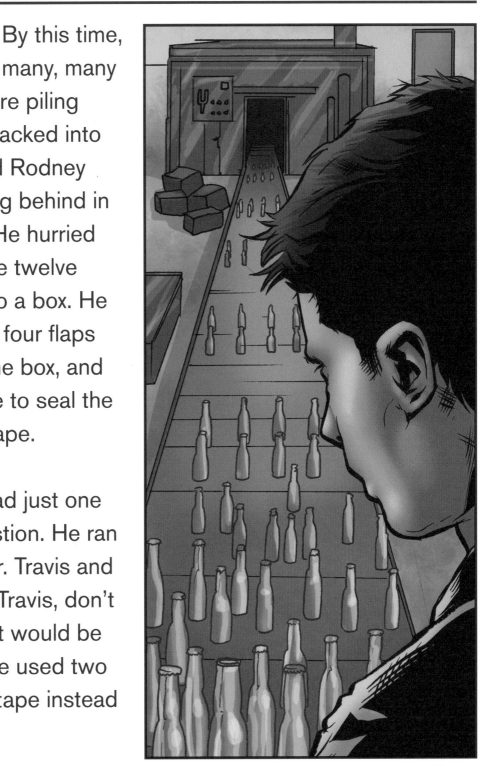

Mr. Travis said, "No, Rodney! One will be fine!" Rodney said, "I just wanted to be sure!"

CHAPTER 5

Rodney ran back to the conveyor belt where more and more bottles were piling up. He had to hurry to get the tape to seal the box. He pulled off a very long piece of tape. He was in such a hurry that he became tangled in the tape.

Mr. Travis heard a very loud crash! He went running to the conveyor belt, and do you know what he found?

Rodney was sitting in a heap at the end of the conveyor belt. He was covered with tape in a tangled mess, and there were broken bottles all around him!

The Job Interview

Ed Tubb needed to hire a new grocery sacker.

The Job Interview

CHAPTER 1

Ed Tubb was the manager of Eat-Rite Grocery Store. He was in charge of hiring all the people who worked in the store.

The person who sacked the groceries for Mr. Tubb decided to quit his job. Ed needed to hire a new person to fill this position.

Several people came to apply for this job. Each person filled out a job application form. Ed looked at all the applications and had interviews with three people.

The Job Interview

Ty was the first person who came for an interview. When Ty walked into Ed's office, there was a cloud like a dust storm all around him. Ty had not taken a bath in a week, and Ed almost fainted because he smelled so bad.

Ty's hair was sticking out all over his head, and there was

spinach in his teeth. He had a silver ring in his nose and a spike through his chin. He must have enjoyed his latest meal because there were food stains all over his shirt.

When Mr. Tubb saw Ty, he couldn't believe his eyes. Needless to say, the interview was very short.

The Job Interview

CHAPTER 3 The second person who came to be interviewed was Barry. Barry loved to talk to people. He liked to get everyone to notice him by talking about bad, violent and gross things. He told Mr. Tubb that his father liked to drink and smoke. He then talked on and on about an accident where a person hit a dog with their car. He told about the blood and guts that were on the road.

The Job Interview

Mr. Tubb told Barry that he had to leave for another meeting because he wanted to get away from Barry as quickly as possible.

CHAPTER 4

Sarah was the last person to interview for the grocery sacking job. She was neatly groomed, calm, quiet and polite. She shook Mr. Tubb's hand,

The Job Interview

introduced herself and was friendly to him. Sarah only talked about nice things like how much she would like the job and how hard she would work for Mr. Tubb.

CHAPTER 5 If you were Ed Tubb, who would you hire for the job?

Social Story Readers

Out of Control

Jack loved to play basketball.

Out of Control

CHAPTER 1

Jack loved to play basketball. He was great at shooting baskets. Jack and his best friend, George, could play basketball for hours, and they never grew tired.

Jack and George started school together in kindergarten and now they were in high school. They had been friends for a long time and had a lot of fun together.

Social Story Readers

Out of Control

CHAPTER 2 George would never forget the time Jack went into the girl's P.E. equipment room to return the baseball bats. Jack accidentally locked himself in. The girls came in the next period to get dressed for P.E. They ran screaming from the room when they saw Jack locked in with the equipment.

Jack remembered when George brought his pet, Gizzard the Lizard, to school. He kept Gizzard in his pocket and he escaped. George did not find Gizzard until he opened his lunch sack in the cafeteria. Just as he was about to take the first bite, two little eyes poked out of his sandwich. It was a very close call for Gizzard that day!

CHAPTER 3

Jack and George got along well together except that Jack had a bad temper. Jack would get really mad for no reason and he would throw a big fit. He would rant, rave, curse and throw things.

Out of Control

When Jack was in kindergarten, it didn't seem so bad. All the little kids threw fits when they didn't get what they wanted. But as they grew older, everyone learned to control themselves except Jack. George still thought of Jack as a good friend, and tried to overlook his bad temper. He usually ignored Jack's tantrums.

CHAPTER 4

One day, George didn't agree with Jack about something, and Jack became so out of control that he actually hit George, his best friend, in the face!

Out of Control

Later, George decided they couldn't be friends anymore. It was sad that their friendship had to end because Jack couldn't control his temper. Sometimes, when people make bad choices, there are consequences that are just as bad!

Chill Out

I WANT GLENDA TO BE MY GIRLFRIEND.

Glenda was the most beautiful girl that Jacob had ever seen.

Chill Out

CHAPTER 1 Jacob went to school every day with the hope that Glenda would notice him. Glenda was the most beautiful girl that Jacob had ever seen. Jacob thought about Glenda all the time. He was always thinking of ways to make her like him.

He sent her roses. He filled her car with balloons. He left notes in her books everyday. When Glenda opened her locker, there was a huge picture of Jacob staring right at her.

He followed her everywhere. If she went around a corner, there was Jacob. If she looked out of her window at home, he would be walking past her house.

Social Story Readers

Chill Out

Jacob called her on the telephone and Glenda talked to him. She said, "Jacob, you are a nice person, but I already have a boyfriend. So I would appreciate it if you wouldn't call me or follow me around anymore. We can just be friends." Jacob answered, "Well, I think you can have two boyfriends."

Chill Out

CHAPTER 3   Instead of listening to Glenda, Jacob continued to call her all day long. She didn't answer the phone, but he called and left messages fifteen times!

Glenda's parents saw all the messages on the answering machine. They asked her about them. Glenda admitted to them that she was starting to become frightened, because Jacob would not leave her alone.

What do you think would be the right thing for Jacob to do?

I'm Not a Chicken, You Turkey!

Carl was lonely.

I'm Not a Chicken, You Turkey!

CHAPTER 1 Carl was lonely. His friend, Neal, moved to a different town and was going to a new school.

Carl decided to hang out with different people and try to find new friends.

He ate lunch with a guy he knew named James. They had a good time at lunch, and afterwards they went outside together. James said, "I usually meet Margaret outside. She is a cool chick!"

Social Story Readers

I'm Not a Chicken, You Turkey!

They found Margaret, and she came over to join them. She said, "Hi, Carl. It's nice to meet you!"

Carl answered, "Yeah, nice to meet you, too!"

While they were all three standing there together, James and Margaret started hugging, kissing and touching each other right in front of Carl.

Carl was so embarrassed! He didn't know where to look or what to do. He decided to leave them and go back into the school. Maybe, this friendship with James wasn't going to work out after all.

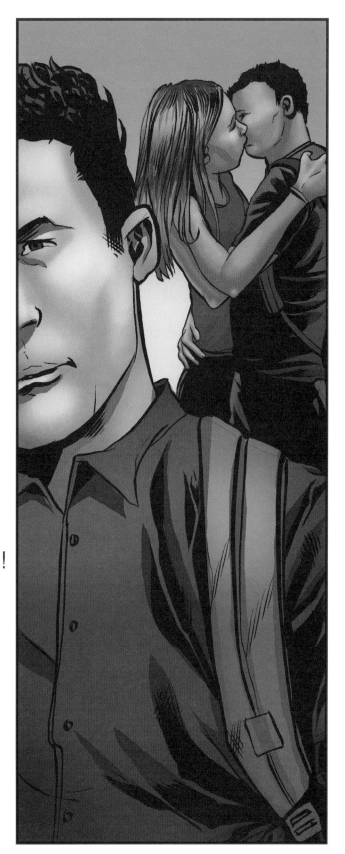

I'm Not a Chicken, You Turkey!

CHAPTER 3

The next day, Carl decided to try again. He had lunch with Charlie and Austin. After lunch, Charlie said, "Let's go in the boy's restroom and smoke a cigarette."

"No! We'll get into big trouble!" Carl said. "You're just a big chicken!" Austin replied.

Carl ignored them and went off to be by himself. Did everybody have poultry on the brain? All they talked about was being with a cool chick or being a big chicken. He was afraid to go to sleep at night, because he had nightmares about beaks and feathers.

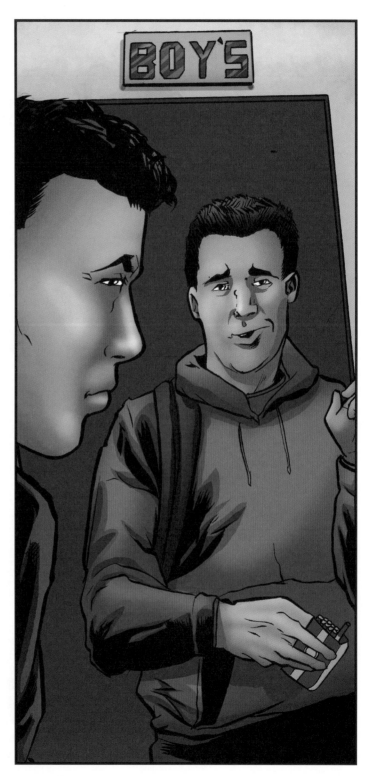

Social Story Readers

I'm Not a Chicken, You Turkey!

Carl started to think that he was the one who didn't fit in with the others. He wanted to do the right things, but he also wanted to have friends.

CHAPTER 4   A few days later, Carl was hurrying to class. He went around a corner, and accidentally ran into Lucas and Kim who were coming from the opposite direction. All their books and papers went flying around like a tornado. They all landed in a heap with Lucas's elbow in Carl's eye and Carl's foot pressing down on Kim's neck.

I'm Not a Chicken, You Turkey!

They helped each other up and picked up all the books and papers together.

Carl said, "Sorry! I didn't mean to knock you down. I was just in a hurry to get to class."

Kim said, "Don't worry, it was our fault, too." Lucas said, "Hey, we have noticed that you were eating by yourself at lunch lately. Would you like to eat with us?"

Carl said, "Sure, I would like that, but I hope they're not serving chicken in the cafeteria."

Social Story Readers

Social Story Readers Dictionary

Aa

accidentally – to do something you did not mean to happen (happening by chance or bad luck)

answer – to reply to a question, to solve a puzzle or problem

application – a form to fill out when asking for a job

appreciate – to be thankful for something

avoid – to stay away from

Bb

barely – almost there, but not quite; just a little

beaks – a hard pointed part of a bird's mouth

behavior – the way a person acts or the actions he takes

Cc

change – make something different

choices – to decide about something after thinking it through

concentrating – to pay attention to; focus on

consequences – something that happens because of an action or choice made

control – to hold back or curb

conveyor – that which carries from one place to another

crocodile tears – crying fake tears to get attention

Dd

decided – to settle a question or argument; to make up your mind

different – changed; not the same as before

directions – the way you go or the way something points

discover – to find out or understand

Ee

equipment – anything needed for a project or activity; tools or supplies

Ff

famous – very well known

favorite – something that you want or love the most

finished – got the job done, the end, it's over or completed

friendship – a relationship with someone you like; a warm feeling between friends

frightened – scared

Gg

goal – something that a person wants or works for

guilty – having done something wrong

Hh

hire – to agree to pay money to someone in return for their work on a job

hope – to want something to happen and to believe that it will

huge – very big

hurry – to speed up, to do something faster or more quickly

Ii

ignore – pay no attention to, do not notice

imagined – to picture something in your mind; to think of something

important – things that matter; something you value or cherish

in charge of – held responsible for a certain job, depended on to do something

independent – to be on your own; able to take care of yourself without a lot of help from others

innocent – blameless, in the clear, doing nothing wrong

interview – a meeting with another person to talk about a job

introduce – tell someone your name

invisible – not able to be seen

Jj

jealous – to want something you don't have

Kk

knuckle – a joint where bones connect in the fingers and hand

Ll

lazy – not wanting to work or do much at all

local – related to a particular place

Mm

manager – a person who has control of other people on a job

messages – words sent from one person to another

miracle – an amazing thing, an awesome sight

mistake – blooper, wrong answer

motion – moving from one place to another, changing positions

mysterious – hard to explain or understand

Nn

nightmare – a bad, scary or frightening dream

notice – to see, watch, or look at; to give attention to

Oo

obsession – to fill the mind in an unhealthy way

opposite – different in every way

ordeal – trouble, hardship, or worry, a nightmare, pain or suffering

Pp

permanent – meant to last for a very long time

permission – when an adult who is in charge says it is OK to do something

position – a job

possible – it can be done or it can happen

poultry – chickens, turkeys, ducks, and other birds raised for food.

promise – give your word, say you will do something

proud – to feel really happy about something you or someone else has done

Rr

relieved – calmed and thankful

reminds – to help a person remember or think of something

replaced – to take something away and put something else in its place

responsibility – a job or thing people can trust you to do

risk – (good risk) to try your best and take a chance; (bad risk) to put yourself and others in danger

Ss

scared – worried, nervous, afraid or frightened

seal – a tight, perfect closure; something that closes

season – a time of the year: spring, summer, fall and winter

shrewd – clever, sharp, bright, smart, intelligent

shy – bashful and quiet

Tt

take advantage of – to help yourself by using someone else

tangled – twisted together, hard to straighten out again

tantrum – a fit

tattle – to tell someone's secrets to a teacher, parent or boss

team – a group of more than one person

temper – An outburst of uncontrolled anger

tornado – a storm with very high winds that travel in circles and do a lot of damage to buildings and trees

Ww

wonder – to think about